英 汉 对 照

口腔临床英语会话集

Easy To Memorize
English Conversation Phrases
In Dental Office

主 编　余立江

编 译　（按姓氏拼音为序）

　　　　董　莹　郭春岚　余立江

审 校　薛　雯

U0224332

中国协和医科大学出版社

图书在版编目（CIP）数据

英汉对照口腔临床英语会话集/余立江主编. —北京：中国协和医科大学出版社，2006.10（2024.6重印）
ISBN 7 – 81072 – 817 – 2

Ⅰ. 口… Ⅱ. 余… Ⅲ. 口腔科学 – 英语 – 口语
Ⅳ. H319.9

中国版本图书馆 CIP 数据核字（2006）第 107565 号

英汉对照
口腔临床英语会话集

| 主　　编：余立江 |
| 责任编辑：严　楠　李春宇 |

出版发行	中国协和医科大学出版社
	（北京市东城区东单三条9号　邮编100730　电话010 – 65260431）
网　　址	www. pumcp. com
经　　销	新华书店总店北京发行所
印　　刷	三河市龙大印装有限公司

开　　本	787 × 1092　1/32
印　　张	4.875
字　　数	40 千字
版　　次	2007 年 1 月第 1 版
印　　次	2024 年 6 月第 16 次印刷
定　　价	18.00 元

ISBN 7 – 81072 – 817 – 2

随着我国改革开放政策的深入，在华居住和来华旅游的外籍人士日渐增多，到医院就诊的外籍人士迅速增加。由此，普及英语会话已成为当务之急。为帮助广大口腔医务工作者学习英语，迅速掌握口腔临床英语会话，我们根据口腔科工作实践编写了这本《口腔临床英语会话集》。

到目前为止，国内尚无口腔专科的临床英语会话书籍，既往前辈们所著均为临床各科综合性会话集。然而各个科室都有自身的专业语言和临床特点，许多医务人员迫切需要一本符合本专业临床需要的工具书。本书正是应目前口腔专业医务工作者的要求，详尽编译了临床工作中可能遇到的各种情况所需语言，包括门急诊接诊病人、诊断、治疗、随访等内容，为临床医师与患者沟通提供便捷的案头资料，并可作为教材供本专业英语语种学生使用。

本书的特点是覆盖面广，包括口腔各专业，用语符合英语语种国家人民的口语习惯，言简意赅，通俗易懂，对应准确，并避免使用生僻词汇，便于使用者快速掌握，是一本实用性很强的书籍。

本书在编译、审校过程中得到口腔科同行及医用英语专业前辈的大力支持和帮助，在此表示衷心的感谢！由于编者水平有限，书中难免会出现错误，敬请广大读者批评指正。

编　者
2006 年 6 月

Contents

（一）Dental workforce

口腔工作者

dentist	口腔医生
dental hygienist	口腔医士
dental technician	口腔技师
dental assistant	口腔医生助理
dental receptionist	口腔收款员

（二）Stomatology

口腔医学

| Clinical dentistry
临床口腔学

preventive dentistry	口腔预防医学
conservative dentistry	牙体保存学
periodontics	牙周病学
endodontics	牙体牙髓病学
prosthodontics	口腔修复学
oral and maxillofacial surgery	口腔颌面外科学
orthodontics	口腔正畸学
paediatriodontics	儿童口腔病学
dental radiology	口腔影像学
dental anesthesiology	口腔麻醉学
geriatric dentistry	老年口腔医学
dentistry for the disabled（handicapped）	残疾人口腔医学
oral diagnosis	口腔诊断学
dental behavioral science	口腔行为科学

II Social dentistry
社会口腔学

community dentistry	社区口腔学
public dental health	大众口腔健康学
dental forensic science	口腔法医学

III Basic dentistry
基础口腔学

oral anatomy	口腔解剖学
oral physiology	口腔生理学
oral biochemistry	口腔生物化学
oral pathology	口腔病理学
oral microbiology	口腔微生物学
dental pharmacology	口腔药物学
dental technology	口腔技工学
dental materials	口腔材料学

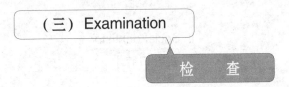

（三）Examination

检 查

chief complaint	主诉
anamnesis	既往史
history of present illness	现病史
family history	家族史
health questionnaire	健康询问
interview	就诊
inspection	检查
palpation	触诊
percussion	叩诊
clinical examination	临床检查
roentgenographic examination	X 线片检查
diagnosis	诊断

（四）Pain

疼　痛

slight pain	轻微痛
moderate（middle）pain	中等痛
severe（violent）pain	剧痛
sharp pain	锐痛
dull pain	钝痛
acute pain	急性疼痛
throbbing（pulsating）pain	跳痛
spontaneous pain	自发痛
continuous pain	持续痛
intermittent pain	间歇痛
cold water pain	冷水痛
biting（occlusal）pain	咬合痛
pain in bed，night pain	夜间痛
oppressive pain	压痛
postoperative pain	术后痛
referred pain	放射痛

（五） Systematic disease

系 统 疾 病

hypertension(high blood pressure)	高血压
hypotension (low blood pressure)	低血压
disease of heart	心脏病
diabetes	糖尿病
disease of liver	肝病
hepatitis	肝炎
disease of kidney	肾病
nephritis	肾炎
gastric ulcer	胃溃疡
appendicitis	阑尾炎
pneumonia	肺炎
tuberculosis	结核病
asthma	哮喘
rheumatic fever	风湿热
arthritis	关节炎
bleeding disorder	凝血障碍
anemia	贫血
hemophilia	血友病

leukemia	白血病
epilepsy	癫痫
neurosis	神经衰弱
cancer	癌症
AIDS（acquired immunodeficiency syndrome）	艾滋病（获得性免疫缺陷综合征）
syphilis	梅毒
gonorrhea	淋病

（六）Dental disease

口腔疾病

dental caries	龋病
pulpitis	牙髓炎
periodontitis	牙周炎
gingivitis	牙龈炎
marginal gingivitis	边缘性牙龈炎
periapical inflammation	根尖周炎
pericoronitis	冠周炎
stomatitis	口腔粘膜炎

cheilitis	唇炎
glossitis	舌炎
recurrent aphtous ulcer	复发性阿弗他溃疡
Behcet disease	贝赫切特病 （原称白塞病）
oral lichen planus	口腔扁平苔藓
chronic discoid lupus erythematosus	慢性盘状红斑狼疮
leukoplakia	白斑
erythroplakia	红斑
burning mouth syndrome	灼口综合征
impacted tooth	阻生齿
congenital anodontia	先天无牙
supernumerary tooth	多生牙
fused teeth	融合牙
aconcial tooth	锥形牙
attrition	磨耗
abrasion	磨损
wedge – shaped defect	楔状缺损
abscess	脓肿
cyst	囊肿
cleft lip	唇裂
cleft palate	腭裂
trismus	牙关紧闭

bruxism, grinding	磨牙症
temporomandibular joint dysfunction	颞下颌关节紊乱病
halitosis	口臭
malocclusion	错𬌗
prognothia	上颌前突
progenia	下颌前突
open bite	开𬌗
deep overbite	深覆𬌗
cross bite	锁𬌗
diastema	牙间隙

（七）Dental treatment

口 腔 治 疗

cavity preparation	窝洞预备
permanent filling	永久充填
temporary filling	暂时充填
temporary sealing	暂封
resin filling	树脂充填
amalgam filling	银汞合金充填

pulp capping	盖髓
pulpotomy	活髓切断术
pulpectomy	牙髓摘除术
root canal treatment	根管治疗
root canal filling	根管充填
tooth brushing instruction（TBI）	刷牙指导
scaling	洁治
topical application of fluoride	表面涂氟
gingivectomy	牙龈切除术
flap operation	翻瓣术
osteoplasty	骨修整术
apicoectomy，apicotomy	根尖切除术
permanent fixation	永久固定
inlay	嵌体
abutment tooth	基牙
cast crown	铸造冠
fixed bridge	固定桥
partial denture	局部义齿
full denture	全口义齿
gum retraction（displacement）	排龈
impression taking	取印模
bite taking	咬合记录
trial application	试戴

occlusal paper	咬合纸
occlusal adjustment（equilibration）	调𬌗
polishing	抛光
cementation（cementing）	粘固
repairing	修理
dental anesthesia	牙科麻醉
topical anesthesia	表面麻醉
infiltration anesthesia	浸润麻醉
tooth extraction	拔牙
suture	缝合
disinfection	消毒
sterilization	灭菌

（八）Names of teeth

牙齿的名称

permanent teeth	恒牙
deciduous teeth（milk teeth）	乳牙
central incisor	中切牙
lateral incisor	侧切牙

cuspid (canine, *eye* tooth)	尖牙
first bicuspid (premolar)	第一前磨牙
second bicuspid (premolar)	第二前磨牙
first molar (six –year molar)	第一磨牙(六龄齿)
second molar	第二磨牙
third molar	第三磨牙
wisdom tooth	智齿

（九）Names of parts

牙 体 解 剖

labial surface (lip side)	唇侧面
buccal surface (cheek side)	颊侧面
lingual surface (tongue side)	舌侧面
palatal surface (inner surface)	腭侧面
occlusal surface (chewing surface)	咬殆面
proximal surface (between the teeth)	邻接面
mesial surface	近中面
distal surface	远中面
pit and fissure, groove	窝沟点隙

interdental area（between the teeth）	牙槽间隔
cervical area	牙颈部
enamel	牙釉质
dentin	牙本质
cementum	牙骨质
pulp	牙髓
pulp horn	髓角
root canal	根管
root apex	根尖
apical foramen	根尖孔
accessory canal	副根管
alveolar bone	牙槽骨
periodontal ligament	牙周韧带
gingival	牙龈
cementoenamel junction	釉牙骨质界

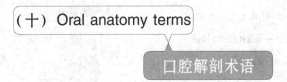

（十）Oral anatomy terms

口腔解剖术语

maxilla（upper jaw）	上颌
mandible（lower jaw）	下颌

the lips	口唇
corner of mouth	口角
fauces	喉头
hard palate	硬腭
uvula	悬雍垂
palatine tonsil	腭扁桃体
palatine rugae	腭皱襞
palatine foveola	腭小凹
floor of the mouth	口底
tongue frenum	舌系带
buccal frenum	颊系带
labial frenum	唇系带
buccal mucosa	颊粘膜
gingivobuccal fold	龈颊沟
nasolabial sulcus	鼻唇沟
temporomandibular joint	颞下颌关节
mandibular condyle	下颌关节突（髁突）
mandibular foramen	下颌孔
naso – auricular line	耳屏鼻翼连线
facial plane	脸面
eye – era plane	眼耳平面
orbital plane	眶平面
rankfort plane	眶耳平面

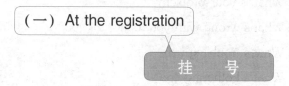

（一） At the registration

挂　　号

1. 我能为您做什么？（您有什么事吗?）

What can I do for you?

May I help you?

Is there any thing we can do for you?

What is it?

How can we help you?

2. 您哪里不舒服？

What is your problem?

What's wrong with you today?

What's troubling you?

What's bothering you?

What seems to be the problem?

What's the matter with you?

What's your complaint?

What are you suffering from?

3. 您要看牙病吗？

Do you want to see a dentist?

4. 您要挂哪个专业的号？

Which speciality do you want to register with?

5. 您要拔牙（补牙）吗？

Do you want to have your tooth pulled (tooth filled)?

6. 补牙？镶牙（做义齿）？还是洗牙（洁牙）？

For a filling? A denture? Or a cleaning?

7. 您以前来过这儿吗？

Have you been here before?

8. 这是您第一次到口腔门诊吗？

Is this your first visit to this dental clinic?

9. 您是初诊病人吗？

Are you a new patient?

10. 谁介绍您来这里的？

Who introduced this clinic to you?

11. 您会说英语吗？

Do you speak English?

12. 您明白我说的话吗？

Do you understand what I'm saying?

Is there anything else you would like me to explain to you?

Should I explain it again?

---

13. 下次请带翻译来。

Please come with your interpreter next time。

---

14. 可以把您的名字告诉我吗？

May I have your name?

---

15. 请拼写您的名字。

Could you spell your name, please?

---

16. 请告诉我您的住址、电话号码、年龄和职业。

May I have your address, telephone number, age and occupation?

What's your address, telephone number, age and occupation, please?

17. 请告诉我您的电话。

Your telephone number, please.

18. 您在这里做什么工作？

What is your work here?

19. 您的年龄？

How old are you?

20. 您是哪年出生的？

When were you born?

21. 请把您的姓名和出生日写在这张卡上。

Please write your name and date of birth on this card.

22. 请写上您的全名。

Please write down your full name.

23. 请填写这张记录卡。

Please fill out this record card.

24. 您有挂号证吗？

Do you have a registration card?

25. 您记得您的挂号证号吗？

Do you remember your card number?

26. 上次您什么时候来的？

When did you come last?

27. 您打算在中国逗留一段时间吗？

Are you going to stay in China for a while?

28. 您将在中国呆多久？

How long will you live in China?

29. 您准备在这里呆多久？

How long do you intend to stay here?

30．您有中国的健康保险吗？

Do you have a Chinese health insurance？

31．请出示您的健康卡。

Please show me your health insurance card.

32．您预约了吗？

Do you have an appointment？

33．今天已经预约满了。

We are fully booked today.

34．您愿意等一会儿吗？

Could you wait for a while？

35．请稍等。

Wait a moment，please.

36．您愿意等几分钟吗？

Would you wait a few minutes？

May I be excused for a while?

---

37. 我很快回来。

I'll come back right away.

---

38. 请把卡放在桌子上等着我叫您。

Please put your card on the desk and wait until we call you.

---

39. 每次您来挂号时，请出示这张卡。

Please show this card at the registration desk every time you come.

---

40. 谁替您付款？

Who is paying?

---

41. 单位给您报销吗？

Can you charge it to your organization?

---

42. 他们给您报销吗？

Will they reimburse you?

43. 请交挂号费。

Please pay for the registration.

44. 这是收据和找回的钱。

Here is your receipt and change.

45. 您有零钱吗？

Do you have any small change?

46. 这是您的挂号证。请不要遗失，每次来时带着它。

This is your registration card. Please don't lose it and bring it here whenever you come.

47. 请在候诊室等待。

Please wait in the waiting room.

48. 请坐。

Please have a seat.

Please sit down.

Would you take a seat?

---

49. 医生很快就会给您看了。

The doctor will see you soon.

---

50. 医生现在正在看病人。

The doctor is now with a patient.

---

51. 该您看病了。

It's your turn now.

---

52. 下一个就轮到您了。

Your turn is next.

---

53. 在您前面还有两个病人。

There are two more patients before you.

54. 我们比预约表慢了些。

We are running a little behind the schedule.

55. 您能等二十分钟吗？

Can you wait for twenty minutes?

56. 您前面那个病人情况较复杂。对不起，您至少还得等半个小时。

The patient before you is a rather complicated case. I'm sorry you will have to wait at least half an hour.

57. 很抱歉，让您等了这么久。

I'm sorry to have kept you waiting so long.

58. 请跟我来。

Please come (in) this way.

Please come with me.

59. 请您进治疗室。

Please come into the treatment room, will you?

（二）Directions for the position,
manner and action

椅位，方式和行为的指导

1. 请您坐这个牙椅。

Please sit down in this chair.

2. 我把牙椅向后倾斜点。

I will lean the chair back.

3. 我将抬高牙椅。

I will bring the chair up.

4. 请您向上些。

Please slide up the chair.

5. 请您向下些。

Please slide down the chair.

....

6. 这种椅位，您感觉舒服吗？

Are you comfortable in this position?

....

7. 我给您系上胸巾。

I'll place an apron on you.

....

8. 我给您解下胸巾。

I'll take your apron.

....

9. 请抬起头。

Please lift your head.

....

10. 请把头向后靠。

Please put your head back.

....

11. 请把头向右转。

Please turn your head to the right.

12.　请把头向左转。

Please turn your head to the left.

13.　请保持头直立。

Please keep your head straight.

14.　请向后仰头。

Please tilt your head back.

15.　请收下颌。

Please tuck your chin.

16.　请张嘴。

Please open your mouth.

17.　请把嘴张大些。

Please open your mouth a little wider.

18. 尽可能张大嘴。

Open your mouth as wide as possible.

---

19. 请保持张嘴状态。

Please keep your mouth open.

---

20. 请闭些嘴。

Please close your mouth a little.

---

21. 请闭嘴。

Please close your mouth.

---

22. 请咬合。

Bite down, please.

---

23. 请咬后牙。

Tap your back teeth together.

---

24. 请左右错殆。

Move your jaw to the right and left.

25. 向前伸下颌。

Slide your lower jaw forward.

26. 请保持咬合状态。

Please keep the teeth together.

27. 放松自己，使自己感觉舒服。

Relax and make yourself comfortable.

28. 请放松舌头。

Please relax your tongue.

29. 请放松下颌。

Please relax your jaw.

30. 请放松肩膀。

Please relax your shoulders.

31. 如果疼痛，请举起您的左手。

Please raise your left hand if you feel pain.

....

32. 请漱口。

Rinse your mouth, please.

（三）Questions about
medical history

既往史的询问

1. 首先，我需要了解您的全身健康状况和过敏史。

First, I will ask you about your general health and allergies.

....

2. 您现在身体状况如何？

Are you in good health now?

How are your health conditions now? (Excellent, Average, Poor)

How is your general health condition at present?

3. 您现在看医生了吗？

Are you under a doctor's care now?

4. 您现在接受治疗了吗？

Are you receiving medical treatment now?

5. 您有什么慢性病？

Do you have any chronic disease?

6. 我想了解您的既往史。

I want to ask you about your medical history.

How have you been?

How have you been feeling in general?

How is your general health?

Have you ever had a serious illness?

Have you suffered from any previous illness?

7. 您有手术史吗？

Have you ever had an operation?

Have you had any operations in the past?

．．．

8．您受过外伤吗？

Have you had any serious accidents or injuries?

．．．

9．您输过血吗？

Have you ever had a blood transfusion?

．．．

10．您有心脏病、肝病和肾病吗？

Do you have or have you ever had the disease of heart, liver and kidney?

．．．

11．您有高血压病史吗？

Are you suffering from hypertension?

Have you ever had high blood pressure?

．．．

12．您有糖尿病吗？

Have you had diabetes?

．．．

13. 您还有其他疾病吗？

Have you had any other illness?

Is there anything else that bothers you?

14. 您发烧了吗？

Do you have a fever?

15. 您的食欲怎样？

How is your appetite?

What is your appetite like?

16. 您有吞咽困难的现象吗？

Do you have any trouble in swallowing food?

17. 您目前服用药物吗？

Are you taking any form of medication regularly?

Are you taking any medicines or drugs?

Do you take any medication regularly?

18. 您怀孕了吗?

Are you pregnant?

19. 您的月经规律吗?

Is your menstrual cycle regular?

How are your periods?

20. 您末次月经是哪天?

When did your last period begin?

21. 您有过敏史吗?

Do you have an allergy?

Are you allergic (sensitive) to anything?

Are you allergic (sensitive) to any particular medicine?

Are there any medications you cannot take?

Have you ever had any reactions to a medicine or a shot?

22. 您用过麻醉药吗?

Have you ever had an injection for anesthesia?

23. 您有过伤口或拔牙创口出血不止的经历吗？

Have you ever had abnormal bleeding from an injury or a tooth extraction?

24. 您有过与治牙相关的并发症吗？

Have you ever had complications from dental treatment?

（四）Questions about general symptoms

一般症状的询问

1. 您哪里不舒服？

What is your trouble (problem)?

What is the matter?

What is wrong with you?

2. 能描述一下您的症状吗？

Would you describe your symptoms?

Tell me what symptoms you have?

Can you tell me more about it?

3. 您第一次发现这种情况是什么时候？

When did you first notice such conditions?

When did the symptom start?

When did you first notice anything wrong?

How and when did your illness begin?

4. 您在其他医院看过吗？

Have you already attended another hospital with your problem?

5. 请告诉我医院的名字、治疗方法和时间。

Please tell me the name of the hospital, the period and the type of treatment you received.

6. 您什么时候接受治疗的？告诉我您的症状。

When were you under the care of the doctor recently, tell me the symptoms you had.

7. 您什么时候肿成这样的?

When did you become swollen up like this?

8. 出血多长时间了?

How long did it bleed?

9. 您最后一次治牙是什么时候?

When did the tooth last have dental treatment?

When was the last time you went to a dental treatment?

10. 最后一次做口腔检查是什么时候?

When was your last dental check-up?

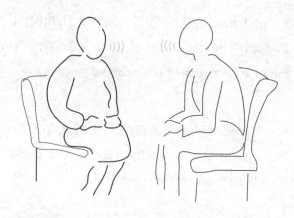

（五）Questions about pain

疼痛的询问

1. 您哪颗牙痛？

Where is the pain?

Where does it hurt?

Which tooth is painful?

2. 这颗牙什么时候开始痛的？

When did the tooth start to hurt?

3. 牙痛多长时间了？

How long have you been with pain?

How long does the pain last?

4. 您能感觉出它是怎么痛的吗？

What kind of pain did you feel?

5. 您曾有过这样的疼痛吗？

Have you ever had a pain like this before?

....

6. 您现在感觉它是怎么痛的？

What kind of pain do you feel now?

....

7. 您能描述一下您的疼痛吗？

Can you describe the pain?

....

8. 哪里最痛？

Where exactly is your pain?

Where do you feel the pain most?

....

9. 疼痛向其他地方放射吗？

Does it spread anywhere else?

Does the pain go anywhere else?

Does the pain stay in one place?

....

10. 它是哪种疼痛？

What kind of pain is it?

What is the pain like?

11.　它是钝痛吗？

Would you describe the pain as a dull pain?

Is it a dull pain?

12.　是锐痛吗？

Is it a sharp pain?

13.　是跳痛吗？

Is it a throbbing pain?

14.　是间断疼痛吗？

Does it come and go?

15.　是突发的疼痛吗？

Did the pain come on suddenly?

16.　什么时候开始痛的？

When did it hurt?

17. 对冷水敏感吗？

Was it sensitive to cold water?

18. 对甜食敏感吗？

Was it sensitive to sweet food?

19. 吃饭和喝水时痛吗？

Did it hurt after eating and drinking?

20. 当您吃热的食物时痛吗？

Did it hurt when you eat hot food?

21. 夜间疼痛会加重吗？

Did it hurt more at night?

Did the pain interfere with sleep?

22. 疼痛使您不能入睡吗？

Did the pain keep you awake at night?

23.　怎样能缓解疼痛呢？

What can make the pain relieved?

Did anything make the pain relieved?

24.　镇痛药能减轻疼痛吗？

Did a painkiller help to relieve the pain?

25.　您经常服用哪种镇痛药？服用的频率？

What sort of painkiller and how often did you take?

26.　您有咀嚼痛吗？

Did pressure make it hurt?

27.　当我叩您的牙时有痛感吗？

Do you feel pain when I tap on this tooth?

28.　当您感觉疼痛时请告诉我。

Let me know if you feel pain.

----

29. 现在疼吗？

Are you in pain now?

....

30. 以前有过这样的疼痛吗？

Have you ever had a pain like this before?

Did it ever hurt before?

....

31. 您有特别痛的地方吗？

Do you have a special pain anywhere?

（六）Questions about periodontal disease

牙周病的询问

1. 您的牙龈曾出过血吗？

Did you have any bleeding from your gums?

....

2. 刷牙时牙龈出血吗？

Did your gums bleed when you brush your teeth?

3. 吃硬食物时，比如说苹果，牙龈出血吗？

Did your gums bleed when you eat hard food, like an apple?

....

4. 这种情况持续多长时间了？

How long have you had this condition?

....

5. 是不明原因的出血吗？

Did the gums bleed for no apparent reason at all?

....

6. 您皮肤上有出血点吗？

Have you noticed any bleeding spots on your skin?

....

7. 您喜欢硬食物还是软食物？

Which do you like better hard or soft food?

....

8. 您偏好什么食物？

Do you have any particular food preferences?

9. 您有过牙龈不舒服的情况吗？

Did your gums ever feel uncomfortable?

10. 您的牙龈肿胀过吗？

Did your gums sometimes swell?

11. 您塞牙吗？

Did food get caught between your teeth?

12. 您感觉哪颗牙松动了？

Do you feel any of your teeth loose?

13. 您感觉牙正在变得松动吗？

Do you feel tooth is getting loose?

14. 您注意到您是否有口呼吸吗？

Do you notice that you breathe through your mouth?

15. 您打呼噜吗？

Do you snore?

16．您有夜间磨牙的习惯吗？

Do you have a habit of grinding your teeth at night?

17．您有紧咬牙的习惯吗？

Do you have a habit of clenching your teeth?

18．您的家人有患牙龈病的吗？

Do you have anyone in your family who had serious gum disease?

19．有医生告诉过您，您患有牙龈炎或牙周炎吗？

Has a dentist ever told you that you have gingivitis or periodontitis?

20．您针对牙龈炎或牙周炎治疗过吗？

Have you ever been treated for gingivitis or periodontitis?

(七) Questions about temporomandibular joint dysfunction

关节功能紊乱的询问

1. 您有以下什么症状：关节弹响，头痛，肩膀僵直或失眠?

Do you have any of the following symptoms: noise in the joints, headache, a stiff shoulder, or sleepless at night?

2. 什么症状最严重?

What is the worst condition now?

3. 什么时候发现下颌有问题的?

When did you find the jaw problem?

Since when have you had this condition?

4. 最初的症状和现在一样吗?

Were the symptoms you had initially the same as they are now?

5. 当你发现下颌有问题时，您还注意到了其他问题吗？

Did you notice any special occasion when you experienced the jaw problem?

....

6. 现在您感觉张口困难吗？

Do you feel that it is difficult to open your mouth now?

....

7. 您什么时候发现张口困难的？

When did you feel it difficult to open your mouth?

....

8. 当您张口时，关节有弹响吗？

Do your joint sound strange when you open your mouth?

....

9. 我按压的部位痛吗？

Do you feel sore here when I press this place?

....

10. 现在关节区疼痛吗？

Do you feel any pain now?

11. 您的咬𬌗力量总是很大吗？

Do you always bite strongly?

12. 您曾被告知有磨牙症吗？

Have you ever been told that you grind your teeth?

13. 您通常用哪一侧咀嚼食物？

On which side of your mouth do you chew most often when you eat food?

14. 直到出现症状时，您通常用哪侧咀嚼食物？

On which side of your mouth did you chew until you felt the symptoms?

（八） Questions about oral mucosa disease

口腔粘膜病的问诊

1. 您有过反复口腔溃疡的历史吗？

Do you have the history of recurrent ulceration?

2. 您多长时间出现一次口腔溃疡？

How often does the ulceration flare up?

3. 每次口腔溃疡大约持续多长时间？

How long does the ulceration usually last?

4. 除了反复口腔溃疡外，您全身还有哪些不舒服？

Do you have any other malaise except for oral recurrent ulceration?

5. 您的疼痛感是像被开水烫过那样的灼烧痛吗？

Is the pain like the feeling scalded by the hot water?

....

6. 您颊粘膜上的白色斑块出现多长时间了？

How long have you had the white plaque on the buccal membrane?

....

7. 您颊粘膜上的糜烂面出现多长时间了？

When did you find the erosion area on your buccal membrane?

....

8. 您舌头痛吗？

Did you feel any pain on your tongue?

....

9. 您的嘴唇什么时候肿的？

When did your lip swell?

....

10. 您的嘴唇总是反复干燥脱屑吗？

Is your lip always desquamative?

11. 您的嘴唇痒吗？

Did you feel itching on your lip?

12. 您感觉口干吗？

Did you have dry mouth?

13. 您口干的现象有多长时间了？

How long have you felt mouth dryness?

14. 您吞咽干性食物需要同时饮水吗？

Did you need drink water to swallow dry food?

（九）X – ray

X 线检查

1. 我将给您的牙齿拍个 X 线片看看牙内情况。

I will take an X – ray to check inside the tooth.

2. 我将给您的颌骨拍个 X 线片以了解颌骨内的情况。

I'll take an X – ray to confirm the condition of your jaw bone.

3. 我想通过 X 线片来看看这颗牙齿的一些细节情况。

I want to examine the tooth in detail by an X – ray.

4. 我将给您的牙齿拍个 X 线片来测量牙根的长度。

I'll take an X – ray to measure the length of the root.

5. 最后一次拍 X 线片是什么时候？

When was the last time you had an X – ray?

6. 请摘下眼镜，取出义齿，把它们放到这儿。

Please take off your glasses, take out your denture, and place them here.

7. 我将给您围上铅围裙。

I'll place a lead apron on you.

8. 我将在您的嘴里放一张感光胶片。

I'll put a film in your mouth.

9. 请按住胶片。

Please press the film for a little while.

10. 您可能感觉有点痛，请坚持。

You may feel a little pain，but please be patient.

11. 请用您的示指抵住胶片。

Please hold the X－ray film with your index finger.

12. 请用您的拇指抵住胶片。

Please use your thumb to hold it.

13. 请别动，坚持一下。

Don't move for a while，please.

14. 请坚持一下。

Please stay still for a moment.

15. 现在，我要照了。

Now, I'm taking an X-ray.

16. 我将取出胶片。

I'll take the film out.

17. 我将拿掉围裙。

I'll take your apron off.

18. 谢谢您的合作。

Thank you for your help.

19. 别忘了您的眼镜和义齿。

Don't forget your glasses and denture.

20. X 线片会几分钟后洗出来。

The X – ray will be developed in a few minutes.

21. 我将阅读您的 X 线片。

I'll examine your X – ray.

22. 请看这张 X 线片。

Please look at this X – ray film.

23. 这张 X 线片显示有个龋洞。

The X – ray shows a cavity.

24. 黑色地方就是龋坏处。

The dark area is where it is decayed.

25. 在大的充填物下方有个继发龋。

There is a decay under a large filling.

26. 龋坏与髓腔非常接近。

The decay is very close to the pulp.

27. 龋坏已经穿髓。

The decay is into the pulp of the tooth.

28. 根尖处有阴影。

There is a dark area around the root tip.

29. 根尖处的骨质已经被吸收。

The bone is absorbed at the apex of the root.

30. 脓肿形成而骨质被破坏。

An abscess has formed and destroyed the bone.

31. 牙齿周围的牙槽骨已经被吸收。

There is bone recession around your teeth.

32. 这颗牙齿的牙根已断为两片。

The root of this tooth is fractured into two pieces.

33. 在您的颌骨内有颗阻生智齿。

You have an impacted wisdom tooth in the bone.

....

34. 第三磨牙阻生是很常见的。

Impacted third molars are common.

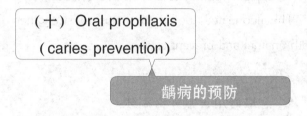

（十）Oral prophlaxis

（caries prevention）

龋病的预防

1. 您听说过氟化物吗？

Have you ever heard of fluoride？

....

2. 氟化物有利于牙齿的再矿化，帮助唾液修复脱矿的牙釉质。

Fluoride is good to tooth remineralization，and can help the saliva to repair the demineralized enamel.

....

3. 氟化物能增加牙齿的硬度，降低酸溶解牙釉质的能力和抑制细菌生长。

Fluoride can increase the hardness of the tooth surface，decrease the acid solubility of the enamel and inhibit the growth of bacteria.

4. 氟化牙膏帮助增强牙釉质和预防龋病。

The fluoridated toothpaste helps to strengthen the tooth enamel and prevent cavities.

5. 您最好用含氟牙膏刷牙。

You had better use fluoridated toothpaste when you brush your teeth.

6. 牙齿表面涂氟可以增强其硬度。

Topical fluoride application makes your teeth strong.

7. 我将给您的牙齿涂氟三分钟。

I will paint fluoride solution on your teeth for three minutes.

8．请不要漱口。

Don't rinse your mouth, please.

9．表面涂氟后三十分钟内不要喝水和吃东西。

You should not drink or eat anything for thirty minutes after fluoride application.

10．乳牙的龋坏进展很快。

Decay of milk teeth advances very quickly.

11．我建议您的孩子用氟化物涂牙齿。

I recommend your child to have topical fluoride application.

12．后牙上的深裂隙容易发生龋坏。

The deep grooves on the back teeth are easy to be decayed.

13. 窝沟封闭剂可以防止细菌和食物进入窝沟腐蚀牙齿。

Sealants keep out the bacteria and food that cause tooth decay.

....

14. 后牙𬌗面上的沟裂是龋病发生的主要部位。

The grooves in the biting surface of molars are major sites for dental decay.

....

15. 刷牙并不能清除所有沟裂内的菌斑。

A toothbrush cannot properly clean all the plaque from these grooves.

....

16. 可以用窝沟封闭剂来保护沟裂。

These grooves can be protected by a hard plastic coating called pit and fissure sealant.

....

17. 窝沟封闭不需要局麻和磨牙。

Fissure sealing requires no injection or drilling.

....

18. 窝沟封闭已被证明可有效预防龋病。

Fissure sealing has been proved to be very effective in preventing dental decay.

19. 我将用树脂材料来封闭这些窝沟，使他们容易清洁。

I'll seal these grooves with this white plastic material to make them easy to be cleaned.

20. 我不需要磨牙。

I won't drill the tooth.

21. 我将把橡皮障放在牙齿上以便获得干燥的环境。

I'll put this rubber dam on the teeth to get a dry field.

22. 现在，我将给您的牙齿做窝沟封闭

Now, I'll seal your teeth.

23. 即使做了窝沟封闭，每餐后刷牙也是非常重要的。

It is very important to brush all your teeth after every meal, even though they have been sealed.

24. 合理的饮食可增强抵抗疾病的能力。

A well balanced diet increases the resistance to disease.

25. 食物对预防龋病是非常重要的。

Food plays an important role in the prevention of dental caries.

26. 龋坏是口腔内细菌形成酸的结果。

Tooth decay is the result of acid formation by bacteria in the mouth.

27. 碳水化合物，尤其是蔗糖容易被细菌作用形成酸。

The fermentable carbohydrate, especially sugar is easily changed into acid by bacteria.

28. 酸溶解牙釉质后形成龋洞。

The acid dissolves the enamel and brings on cavities.

29. 菌斑中的细菌利用蔗糖形成酸，而酸会腐蚀牙釉质。

Bacteria in the plaque use sugars to form acid and the acid dissolves the enamel.

30. 正确的刷牙，减少甜食的摄入，规律的口腔检查和窝沟封闭对预防龋病都是非常重要的。

Brushing the teeth properly, cutting down the sweet food, receiving regular dental check-ups and application of fluoride and fissure sealing are all important to the prevention of tooth decay.

31. 龋病可以通过家庭和专业的护理来预防。

Dental caries can be prevented with a combination of home care and professional care.

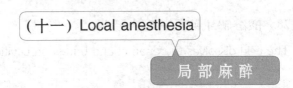
（十一）Local anesthesia

局 部 麻 醉

1. 当我钻牙时您感觉痛吗？如果痛，我将给您打针麻药。

Are you feeling a pain when I use the drill? Then I will use an injection for anesthesia.

2. 龋洞很深，在钻牙前我将给您打一针局麻药。

The decay is very deep, so I will use a local anesthetic before drilling.

3. 您以前对局麻药有什么不良反应？

Have you ever had any adverse reactions to a local anesthetic?

4. 您以前有不良反应吗？

Did you experience side effects?

5. 您有过敏史吗？

Do you have allergies?

6. 您没有高血压病史，对吗？

You are not suffering from hypertention，are you?

7. 请缓慢深呼吸。

Please breathe deeply and slowly.

8. 请放松。

Please relax yourself.

9. 我将在您的牙龈表面涂些药物。

I'll put some medicine on the surface of your gums.

10. 我将用表麻药来麻醉您的牙龈。

I will apply a topical anesthetic to numb the surface of the gum.

11. 表麻将减少注射的疼痛。

Topic anesthetic will lessen the discomfort of the injection.

12. 当我注射麻药时，您可能会感觉到有点针刺感。

You may feel a little sting when I give the injection.

13. 您的嘴唇和舌头麻了吗？

Are your lips and tongue numb?

14. 感觉如何？

How do you feel?

15. 告诉我，它还痛吗？

Tell me if it's still sensitive.

16. 四分钟左右麻药就会起作用。

The anesthetic will take effect in about four minutes.

We will wait about four minutes for the anesthetic to take effect.

17. 两三小时后麻醉效果会消失。

The anesthetic will wear off in about two or three hours.

....

18. 麻木的感觉会持续两三个小时。

The numb feeling will continue for two or three hours.

....

19. 当吃东西时，注意别咬到嘴唇和舌头。

While eating, please be careful not to bite on your lips or tongue.

....

20. 等到麻木的感觉消失后再进食。

Please eat food, after the numb feeling is gone.

(十二) General explanations of treatment

治 疗 的 说 明

1. 我将向您说明治牙过程。

I will explain the treatment procedures for your teeth.

2. 今天我将做如下治疗。

Today I will do the following treatment.

3. 今天我将修复您的下后牙。

Today，I will restore your lower molar (back tooth).

4. 我将为您治疗有个大龋洞的那颗牙。

I will treat the tooth with the largest cavity.

5. 您准备好了吗？

Is that all right with you?

6. 到下次复诊时我将做诊疗计划。

I will make a diagnosis and treatment plan till next appointment.

....

7. 下次复诊时，我想与您讨论治疗计划。

Next time，I want to discuss the treatment schedule with you.

....

8. 吸唾器会吸出您口腔中的唾液。

This aspirator will remove the saliva from your mouth.

....

9. 请向左转头。

Please turn your head to the left.

....

10. 请漱口。

Please rinse your mouth.

....

11. 治疗过程中牙齿可能敏感。

The tooth may be sensitive during treatment.

12. 当钻您的牙时，您会感觉有点振动。

During the drilling of your tooth, you may feel the vibration a little.

13. 钻牙可能会使您感觉点疼痛。

Drilling may hurt you a little bit.

14. 痛吗？

Do you feel any pain?

15. 如果感觉到痛，请举手。

If you feel pain, please raise your hand.

16. 感觉怎样？

How are you feeling?

17. 告诉我您是否感觉不舒服。

Tell me if you feel uncomfortable.

18. 病情不严重。

It is not so serious.

19. 您很快就会好的。

You will soon feel better.

20. 每个人看牙病时都会有点紧张。

Everyone is a little nervous when they have dental treatment.

21. 别担心。

Don't worry.

22. 一切正常。

There is nothing abnormal about that.

23. 不会痛的。

It won't hurt.

24. 很快就会结束。

It will soon be finished.

（十三）Conservative treatment

保 存 治 疗

1. 您的前牙间有两个龋洞。

There are two cavities between your front teeth.

2. 旧充填物与牙体之间有缝隙。

There is a crevice between your teeth and the old filling.

3. 您的充填物已经掉了吗？

Did your filling come out?

4. 金属嵌体脱落了吗？

Did you lose a metal inlay?

5. 前牙切缘已被磨去了一薄层。

The tip of the front tooth has been slightly chipped.

....

6. 预备好的牙很容易被修复。

The chipped tooth can be restored easily.

....

7. 充填物需要更换。

The filling needs replacing.

....

8. 这颗牙需要重新治疗。

The tooth is in need of retreatment.

....

9. 这个龋洞并不深，很容易被充填。

It is not a deep cavity, and can be filled easily.

....

10. 我会用白色树脂材料来充填前牙。

I'll make a white composite resin filling for your front tooth.

11. 因为树脂材料与前牙颜色相同，所以经常被用来修补前牙。

Composite resin is often used in the front tooth, because its color is the same as the teeth.

12. 树脂充填物不易识别。

The resin filling will be unnoticeable.

13. 充填物的颜色与您的牙齿色泽相匹配。

The filling will be matched to the color of your teeth.

14. 因为这是个小的龋洞，所以我用树脂充填。

As it is a small cavity, I will put a resin filling.

15. 今天我将做一个临时充填。

I will put a temporary filling today.

16. 我认为金属材料比树脂材料的硬度要大。

I think it is stronger to use metal restoration than to place resin.

17. 医疗保险不包括金铂合金嵌体治疗。

Health insurance does not cover gold and platinum inlay treatment.

....

18. 我将为您做一个塑料临时冠。

I'll put a plastic temporary crown on the teeth.

....

19. 如果在下次复诊前临时冠掉了，请与我们联系。

If the temporary crown comes off before your next appointment, please contact us.

....

20. 今天，我将去掉临时牙冠换上金冠。

Today I will remove the temporary crown, and set a gold crown.

....

21. 我将在您的嘴里放个棉卷。

I'm going to put a cotton roll in your mouth.

....

22．我将用气枪吹干您的牙齿。

I'm going to dry the tooth by blowing air on to it.

....

23．我将用粘接剂粘固冠。

I'll fix the crown with cement.

....

24．我将把冠向下压一点。

I'll push the crown down slightly.

....

25．您能紧咬这个木棍吗？

Could you bite firmly on this wood stick？

....

26．请咬到粘接剂凝固为止。

Until the cement is set，please keep your teeth together.

....

27．我将取出棉卷。

I'll take the cotton out.

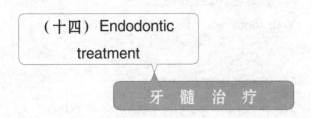

（十四）Endodontic
treatment

牙 髓 治 疗

1. 我将对这颗牙做牙髓活力测试。

I will do a pulp test on this tooth.

2. 我想给这颗牙进行牙髓活力测试，看看牙髓
是否正常。

I'll do a pulp test on the tooth to find out whether the
pulp is healthy.

3. 这个仪器对牙髓有点刺激。

This instrument will stimulate pulp a little bit.

4. 当您感觉不舒服时告诉我，我就会立刻
停止。

Tell me if you feel uncomfortable, then I'll stop immediately.

5. 您的牙神经已坏死。

Your tooth didn't respond to the test.

6. 牙神经因感染已坏死。

The nerve seems to be dead from infection.

7. 龋坏是脓肿的原因。

The decay was the cause of the abscess.

8. 根管治疗是必需的。

Root canal treatment is necessary.

9. 为了消除疼痛，根管治疗是必需的。

In order to remove the pain, it is necessary to do a root canal treatment.

10. 为了保留这颗牙，根管清洗和消毒是很重要的。

It is important to clean and disinfect the root canal in order to save the tooth.

11. 我用牙钻去除龋坏物并扩大根管。

I will drill the tooth to remove the decay and enlarge the root canal from now on.

12. 我不建议拔牙。

I don't recommend extraction.

13. 根管治疗可以保留这颗牙。

Root canal treatment will probably save that tooth.

14. 成功的机会大于百分之九十。

The chance for success is better than ninety percent.

15. 当根管治疗时需要橡皮障。

We use rubber dam when we do root canal treatment.

16. 为了能获得一个清洁干燥的工作环境，我将给您的牙上放上橡皮障。

To provide a clean and dry working field on the tooth, I'll put this rubber dam on your tooth.

17.　我在您的口腔里放入橡皮障，以防唾液弄湿牙齿。

I will put the rubber dam in your mouth to prevent saliva from running over the teeth.

18.　您不会感觉到疼痛，但您将会感觉到您的牙龈有些紧。

You won't feel pain, but perhaps you'll feel tight on your gum.

19.　如果您想告诉我什么事，请举手。

If you want to tell me anything, just raise your hand.

20.　如果您感觉不舒服，请用举手示意。

If you feel uncomfortable, please tell me by raising your hand.

21.　根管治疗的方法如下。

The methods of root canal treatment are as the following.

22. 我将去除所有腐败物。

I'll remove all the decay of the tooth.

23. 我将在您的牙齿上钻个小眼。

I'll make a small opening in the top of your tooth.

24. 通过这个小眼可以使脓液引出。

This opening in the tooth will let the infection drain.

25. 我将清理预备根管。

I'll clean and smooth the root canal.

26. 我将冲洗根管。

I'll irrigate to clean the root canal.

27. 我将在根管里放些药物来消除感染。

I'll treat the infection by putting medication in the tooth.

28. 我将通过根管来消除牙根尖感染。

I'll disinfect the focus at the root tip through your root canal.

....

29. 给这颗牙暂封。

A temporary filling will be placed on the tooth.

....

30. 今天牙神经已被切断，这可能会使您感觉有点痛。

Today the nerve has been cut, so you may feel a little painful.

....

31. 在一段时间里，您的牙齿可能会感觉不舒服。

Your tooth may be uncomfortable for a while.

....

32. 这颗牙可能会使您有异样的感觉。

You may feel a strange sensation in your teeth.

....

33. 好点了吗？

Is it getting better?

34. 还痛吗?

Do you feel pain any more?

35. 根管内看起来已干净。

The inside of the root canal seems like clean.

36. 我认为炎症已消除。

I think the infection has gone.

37. 根管内所有炎性物质被去除后,我将用橡胶材料充填您的根管。

After all the infected tissue has been removed, I will fill the canal with rubber material.

38. 我将充填根管。

I'll put a filling in the root canal.

39. 充填物将封住根管,避免其再次感染。

The filling will seal the canal and prevent it from being infected again.

40. 根充后的牙会改变颜色。

The tooth with a root canal filling sometimes changes its color.

41. 我们可以漂白牙齿。

We can bleach the tooth.

42. 为去除感染的根尖，根尖切除术是必需的。

Apicoectomy is necessary to remove the infected root tip.

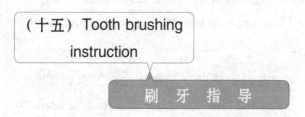

（十五）Tooth brushing
instruction

刷 牙 指 导

1. 一天刷几次牙？

How many times do you brush your teeth in a day？

2. 什么时候刷牙？

When do you brush your teeth？

3. 您用哪种牙刷？

What kind of toothbrush do you use？

4. 您怎么刷牙？

How do you brush your teeth？

Can you tell me average pattern of your bushing your

teeth？

5. 您怎么刷牙，刷多长时间？

How and how long do you brush your teeth?

6. 可以给我做个示范您在家怎么刷牙吗？

Show me how you brush your teeth at home?

7. 请拿着镜子看看自己的口腔。

Please hold this hand mirror and look in your mouth.

8. 您看见您的牙龈很红了吗？

Can you see the redness in your gums?

9. 您看见又红又肿的牙龈了吗？

Do you see how red and inflamed you gums are?

10. 菌斑显示液可以显示出哪里有菌斑。

The plaque disclosing solution shows where the plaque is.

11. 现在我将在您的牙齿上涂菌斑显示液。

Now I will put the red disclosing solution on your teeth.

12. 请含菌斑液三十秒。

Please swish this red solution in your mouth for thirty seconds.

13. 请用水漱口。

Please rinse your mouth once with water.

14. 您看见牙齿红染的地方了吗？

Can you see the red stains on your teeth?

15. 红染的地方就是菌斑。

This red stain is dental plaque.

16. 牙龈缘有很多菌斑。

You have much dental plaque at your gum line.

17. 这说明有些地方您没刷到。

This shows where you have not brushed properly.

18. 有效的刷牙和使用牙线可以去除菌斑。

Plaque can be removed by effective tooth brushing and dental flossing.

19. 让我们从镜子里看看是否您牙上的所有红染斑块已被去除。

Let's look in the mirror and see if you have removed all the red stains from your teeth.

20. 现在，我将在模型上向您展示如何刷牙。

Now, I will show you how to brush your teeth using this dental model.

21. 请像我这样把牙刷放在牙龈与牙齿的联合部位。

Place the toothbrush at the junction of the gums and the teeth like this.

22. 刷毛与牙龈缘呈九十度。

Place the bristles of the brush ninety degrees to the gumline.

23. 用短距离、振动的力量前后移动牙刷。

Move the toothbrush back and forth with short, vibrating strokes.

24. 水平震动牙刷，用轻微的压力去除牙菌斑。

Vibrate the toothbrush horizontally, using gentle pressure to remove the plaque.

25. 向牙尖部旋转牙刷。

Rotate the brush towards the tips of the teeth.

26. 刷上颌牙牙刷应向下移动，刷下颌牙牙刷应向上移动。

Please move the brush downwards on the upper teeth and upwards on the lower teeth.

27. 每个部位应刷十次。

Move it in a circular motion about ten times at the same place.

....

28. 您应该用含氟牙膏正确刷牙。

You should brush your teeth properly, using the toothpaste containing fluoride.

....

29. 含氟牙膏帮助加强牙釉质预防龋齿。

The toothpaste containing fluoride helps to strengthen the tooth enamel and prevent cavities.

....

30. 每次饭后您都应该刷牙。

You should brush your teeth after every meal.

....

31. 请用硬一点的牙刷。

Please use a hard toothbrush.

....

32. 尼龙牙刷较天然毛发牙刷好。

Nylon bristle brushes are better than natural hair brushes.

33. 牙刷头的长度应是示指和中指宽度之和。

The length of the bristles row on the head of the toothbrush should be as long as the width of the index and middle fingers together.

34. 当牙刷毛变弯曲时您应该更换牙刷。

You should change your brush when the bristles get frayed.

35. 一个月应更换一次牙刷。

Your brush should be replaced about once every mouth.

36. 牙线是用来清洁牙间隙的。

Dental floss is used to clean between your teeth.

37. 首先准备四十厘米长的牙线。

First take about forty centimeters of floss.

38. 像这样把牙线绕在中指上。

Wrap the floss around your middle fingers like this.

39. 通过示指和拇指的牵拉来控制牙线。

Control the floss by pinching it with index fingers and thumbs like this.

40. 一个手指在口内，另一个在口外。

Put one finger in the mouth, and the other outside.

41. 在每个牙的各个面上上下摩擦。

Use an up–and–down scraping motion on the sides of each tooth.

42. 如果您的牙间隙较大，最好应用间隙牙刷。

If your interdental space is large, you had better use interdental brush to clean between the teeth.

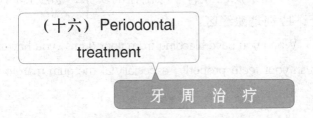

（十六）Periodontal treatment

牙 周 治 疗

1．健康的牙龈质地坚韧并且是粉红色的。

Healthy gums are firm and pink.

....

2．早期牙龈炎的特征是：压痛、肿胀和牙龈出血。

The first stage of gingivitis is characterized by tender,
swollen and bleeding gums.

....

3．下一个阶段牙龈开始退缩。

In the next step, the gums may begin to recede.

....

4．接下来牙齿会因为牙周支持骨的丧失而松动。

In the advanced stage, teeth become loose because
of destruction of the supporting bone.

5. 如果您已经有牙龈出血的现象，您应正确刷牙，特别是龈缘区。

When you have bleeding from your gums, you have to brush your teeth properly, especially at the gum margin.

6. 牙龈有炎症时您应避免使用硬毛牙刷。

You should avoid using a hard toothbrush when your gums are inflamed.

7. 不正确的刷牙方式会导致牙龈退缩和牙体磨耗。

Incorrect tooth brushing causes gum recession and tooth abrasion.

8. 每天刷牙的习惯对维持牙周健康很重要。

Daily brushing habit is important to maintain the periodontal health.

9. 您是否了解如何预防牙周疾病？

Have you ever heard about prevention of periodontal disease?

10. 牙周炎是慢性疾病。

Periodontitis is a chronic disease.

11. 细菌是牙齿龋坏、牙龈疾病和牙石形成的重要原因。

Bacteria are the most important cause of tooth decay, gum disease and calculus formation.

12. 您牙齿周围的牙龈和牙槽骨正在退缩。

The gums and bone are receding around your teeth.

13. 敏感的牙根暴露了。

The sensitive root is exposed.

14. 当牙槽骨降低后牙齿开始松动。

The teeth get loose when the bone recedes.

15. 牙龈疾病可以引起口腔异味。

Bad breath can be caused by gum diseases.

16. 牙龈深部的间隙称为牙周袋。

The deep spaces under the gums are called pockets.

17. 牙周袋的探诊对评价您的牙周状况很重要。

Probing the pockets is important to evaluate your periodontal condition.

18. 牙周袋内通常会存留食物残渣、细菌和牙石。

There are always food, bacteria and calculus in the pockets.

19. 当存在深牙周袋时您无法有效清洁牙齿。

You can't clean the teeth effectively when there are deep pockets.

20. 您可以用牙刷和牙线清除菌斑，但是清除不了牙结石。

You can remove the plaque with a tooth brush and dental floss, but you can't remove the calculus.

21. 您的牙上有很多烟斑。

There is much tobacco stain on your teeth.

....

22. 您一天抽几根烟?

How many cigarettes do you smoke in a day?

....

23. 建议您戒烟。

Please give up smoking.

....

24. 您牙面上坚硬粗糙的染色就是牙结石。

The hard and rough stain is dental calculus (tartar).

....

25. 主要是唾液中的钙离子沉积在牙面上的软垢中形成了牙结石。

It is mainly calcium from the saliva which has formed hard deposits on the teeth.

....

26. 牙结石会刺激牙龈。

Dental calculus irritates the gums.

....

27. 牙周刮治是治疗牙周炎的一种方法。

Scaling is one of the treatments of periodontitis.

28. 如果没有深牙周袋和牙槽骨的吸收，通过有效的刷牙和牙周刮治您的牙龈将恢复健康。

If you don't have deep pockets and bone recession, your gum will be cured with effective tooth brushing and scaling.

29. 您最后一次由牙医洁牙是什么时候？

When was the last time you had your teeth cleaned by a dentist or a dental hygienist?

30. 我将给您清理牙结石。

I will remove the tartar from your teeth now.

31. 我将用超声工作尖给您清洁。

I will use an ultrasonic scaler.

32．超声洗牙时会发出嗡嗡声，产生水雾，并震碎牙结石。

It makes a buzzing noise, sprays a mist of water and breaks up the calculus.

33．如有疼痛请告诉我。

Let me know if you feel any pain.

34．我将给您的牙齿抛光使牙体表面光滑。

Now I will polish your teeth to make them smooth.

35．洗完牙后牙齿会出现对冷热食物敏感的现象。

The teeth may become sensitive to hot and cold food for a while.

36．我将用氟给您的牙齿脱敏。

I will put the fluoride to remove the sensitivity.

37. 敏感的现象一到两周后会消失。

The sensitivity will disappear in one week or two.

38. 刮匙对清除深牙周袋内的牙结石和病变组织是必需的。

Curettage is necessary to remove the calculus and diseased tissue from deep pockets.

39. 如有深牙周袋，可以通过牙周手术切除少许牙周的牙龈组织。

If you have deep pockets, you might need a surgery to remove some of the gum tissue around your teeth.

40. 可以通过翻瓣手术消除深牙周袋。

We will remove the deep pockets by flap operation.

41. 殆垫可以防止夜磨牙。

A night guard will prevent you from grinding your teeth.

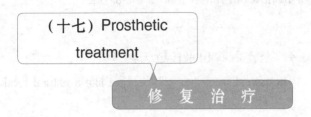

（十七）Prosthetic treatment

修 复 治 疗

| Prosthetic treatment of teeth defection
牙体缺损的修复

1．经过根管治疗的牙齿发生折裂的可能性比较大。

A tooth after root canal treatment is more likely to fracture.

....

2．经过根管治疗的牙齿最好进行桩冠修复保护患牙。

It will be helpful to insert a metal core into the tooth and make a crown after root canal therapy.

....

3．我建议您用烤瓷冠修复前牙而不是金属冠。

I recommend a porcelain fused to metal crown for

your front tooth rather than a metal one.

....

4. 全瓷冠看起来接近天然牙。

The porcelain crown will look just like a natural tooth.

....

5. 前牙的美观很重要。

The appearance of the front teeth is very important.

....

6. 金冠修复不在医保治疗项目之内。

Gold crown is non – insurance treatment.

....

7. 牙冠一星期之后做好。

The crown can be made completely after one week.

....

8. 由于患牙非常薄弱，需要放置桩核。

It is necessary to place a core, as the tooth is very weak.

....

9. 我将在牙内放置桩核以起到支持作用。

I'll put a core into the tooth to support it.

10. 我要在已经充填过的根管中放置金属桩。

I have to put a metal core into the root canal after root canal filling.

11. 在取桩前我要进行牙体预备。

At first, I'll prepare the tooth before making a core.

12. 我将把暂时冠取下。

I'm going to take the temporary crown off.

13. 我将把冠粘固在你的牙上。

I'll fix the crown on your tooth.

‖ Prosthetic treatment of dental arch defection and absent
牙列缺损和缺失的修复

1. 有两种修复缺失牙的方法，一种是可摘活动义齿，另一种是固定义齿。

There are two types of false teeth to replace the lost teeth, one is removable type and the other is fixed type.

2. 与可摘义齿相比，固定桥的基牙需要被磨除更多的牙体组织以为修复体留出间隙。

To make a fixed bridge, we have to prepare more teeth tissue to leave more space, compared with making a removable denture.

3. 这是您第一次戴义齿吗？

Is this the first time you have a denture?

4. 金属基托义齿很贵，但它比较结实且厚度较薄，能传导食物的温度。

The metal plate denture is very expensive. It is not only tough and thin, but also can conduct the temperature of the food.

5. 塑料基托义齿相对便宜，但它较金属基托厚，您不能像戴金属基托义齿那样很好的感觉食物的温度。

The plastic plate denture is cheap, but it will be thicker than the metal plate denture and you can't feel the temperature of food as well as with the metal one.

6. 医疗保险不包括金属基托义齿。

Health insurance does not pay for metal base dentures.

....

7. 这次您想用什么材料？

This time, what kind of material do you prefer?

....

8. 我们可以制作一个即刻义齿。

We can make an immediate denture.

....

9. 拔牙的当天就可以有一个即刻义齿的戴入。

An immediate denture can be inserted on the same day of the tooth extraction.

....

10. 这个义齿可以修理。

This denture can be repaired.

....

11. 制作一副新义齿较修理旧义齿好。

It is better to make a new denture than to repair the old one.

12. 为了制作全口义齿，我将取模灌制研究模型。

To make upper and lower full dentures, I'll take impression for study models.

....

13. 我将在研究模型上设计您的义齿。

I'll design your denture on the study model.

....

14. 为了义齿的稳定，我将把您的牙磨去一点。

To make your denture stable, I'll grind your teeth a little.

....

15. 您能正常的咀嚼吗？

Can you chew properly?

....

16. 您感觉咬合时有高点吗？

Do you feel a high spot on the tooth?

....

17. 慢慢的闭上嘴，告诉我哪颗牙齿先接触。

Close your mouth slowly and tell me which tooth touches first.

18. 请用两侧同时咬这张红纸。

Please bite this red paper on both sides together.

19. 请轻轻咬牙。

Please bite on it gently.

20. 请咬紧牙齿。

Please tap your teeth together.

21. 当咬牙时向右滑动下颌。

Please slide your jaw to the right while you're biting.

22. 请从一侧向另一侧滑动下颌。

Please slide your jaw from side to side.

23. 请向前滑动下颌。

Please slide your jaw to the front.

24. 您感觉哪里先接触？

Do you feel it a little high anywhere?

25. 咬合时有什么不舒服吗？

Do you feel any discomfort for occlusion?

26. 我将把充填物磨低点然后抛光它。

I'll grind the filling down a little, and polish it.

27. 我将给您试戴义齿然后把它调整到适合您的口腔。

I'll try the denture in and adjust it to fit your mouth.

28. 您感觉痛吗？

Do you feel any pain?

29. 让我检查哪里有痛点。

Let's check where you feel pain.

30. 我将磨去少量痛点处的基托。

I'll grind the point a little.

31. 现在感觉怎样？

How do you feel now?

32. 我将调改卡环。

I'll adjust the clasp by grinding.

33. 我磨掉了一些高点，还感觉痛吗？

I ground some points, do you feel pain any more?

34. 请慢慢的闭上嘴。

Please close your mouth slowly.

35. 义齿需要调改几次才能适合您的口腔。

We are going to adjust the denture a few more times
to fit your mouth.

36. 如果您有任何不舒服，请让我知道。

If you have any strange feeling, please let me know about it.

....

III Impression taking
取 印 模

1. 请咬紧蜡片。

Please bite on the wax firmly.

....

2. 请保持一会咬牙状态。

Please keep your teeth together for a while.

....

3. 好，让我们来挑选义齿的颜色。

Well, let's select the color and shade of the teeth for your denture.

....

4. 我将进行比色。

I will do the color matching.

....

5.　您认为义齿设计得如何？

What do you think about this design of the denture.

6.　让我们试戴义齿。

Let's try in this denture.

7.　您对义齿的设计有什么感觉？

How do you feel about this design of the denture?

8.　义齿非常适合您，是这样的吗？

The denture fits perfectly, doesn't it?

9.　为了制定治疗计划，我将为您灌制一副石膏模型。

We will make a plaster model of your teeth for the treatment plan.

10.　为灌制一副研究模型，我将给您的牙齿取印模。

I'll take an impression of your teeth for a study model.

11. 现在我将给您的牙齿取模。

I will now take an impression of your teeth.

12. 待牙龈愈合后我们再取模。

We will wait for the gums to heal before we take the impressions.

13. 我将为嵌体取模。

I will take an impression for an inlay.

14. 我将为制作核取模。

I'll take an impression of this tooth for making a core.

15. 我将为制作牙冠灌制牙模型。

I'll make a model of the teeth for making a crown.

16. 我将为制作义齿灌制牙模型。

I'll make a model of the teeth for making a denture.

17. 首先，我将调改托盘使它适合您的牙弓形态。

First, I'll adjust the tray to fit the size of your mouth.

18. 这次，我将用个别托盘为您取模。

This time I'll take an impression of your mouth by u-sing this individual tray.

19. 我将给您试戴和调改个别托盘。

I'll try in and adjust this individual tray.

20. 我将在您的口腔中试个别托盘，您感觉痛吗？

I'm going to try this tray in your mouth. Well, do you feel any pain?

21. 然后，我给您取模。

Then I'll take an impression.

22. 请张大嘴。

Please open your mouth wide.

23．印模材料会由软渐渐变硬。

At first, the material will be soft, then little by little, it will harden.

....

24．您可能会感觉有异味，请忍耐下。

You may feel it has a strange taste, but please be patient.

....

25．请用鼻子深呼吸。

Please breathe deeply through your nose.

....

26．请用鼻子呼吸一会儿。

Please breathe through your nose for a while.

....

27．请放松。

Please relax yourself.

....

28．请放松嘴唇。

Please relax your lips.

....

29. 当我把托盘放入您的口腔后，请您伸出舌头。

Just after I place the tray in your mouth, please stick your tongue out.

....

30. 请您的舌头左右运动。

Please move your tongue from side to side.

....

31. 请尽量把您的嘴唇向前伸。

Please extend your lip forward as far as possible.

....

32. 我会轻轻地牵拉您的嘴唇和颊部。

I'll pull your lip and cheek a little.

....

33. 左右滑动您的下颌。

Move your jaw to the right and left.

....

34. 我将取出托盘。

I'll remove the tray.

....

35. 我将用力取出托盘。

I'll take the tray out with some power.

36. 请漱口。

Please rinse your mouth.

(十八) Dental implantation

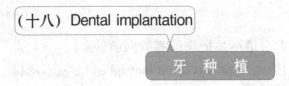

牙 种 植

1. 种植牙可以替代缺失牙。

Implants are used to replace missing teeth.

2. 种植是一种治疗方法：首先在颌骨体上钻一个洞，然后植入金属牙根，最后在牙根上放上一种义齿。

Implantation is the way of the treatment to make a hole on the jaw bone, to put a metal basement and place a kind of denture on it.

3. 为了把种植体植入颌骨，外科手术是必需的。

A surgery is necessary to insert implants into your jaw bone.

4. 手术前必须有些检查。

To receive an operation, you must have some examinations.

5. 您是否适合种植牙治疗取决于检查结果。

It depends on the result of the examination, whether you can have implant treatment or not.

6. 与活动义齿相比，种植牙与天然牙有更相似的功能。

The implant has more similar biting functions to natural teeth than removable dentures.

7. 医疗保险不包括种植治疗。

Health insurance does not cover implant treatment.

8. 种植治疗后需要一段时间才能达到舒适效果。

It takes much time to get comfortable condition after implant treatment.

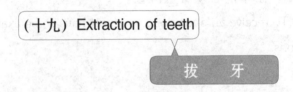

（十九）Extraction of teeth

拔　牙

1. 即使我们保留这颗牙齿，它也没什么功能了。

Even if we keep it in your mouth, the tooth won't work properly any more.

2. 这颗牙齿最好拔除。

This tooth had better be pulled out.

3. 即使我们治疗好了这颗牙齿，它也不会保留多长时间的。

Even if we treat it, it won't work for long.

4. 这颗智齿与上颌牙并没有好的咬合关系。

This wisdom tooth doesn't work in proper occlusion with the upper tooth.

......

5. 您的牙齿在急性炎症期，所以我们不能拔除它

Now, your tooth condition is in status of acute inflammation, so I won't pull it out.

......

6. 我给您开些抗生素，待炎症消退后，我们再拔牙。

I'll give you antibiotics, please take them. After getting a good condition, we will pull it out.

......

7. 待肿胀消退后，我们再拔牙。

We had better wait until the swelling has gone down.

......

8. 待症状消失后，我们再拔牙。

We should wait until the symptoms disappear.

......

9. 拔牙前最好有血常规检查。

It is better to have a blood test before the extraction.

10. 我将给您注射点麻药来减轻疼痛。

I'll give you an anesthetic to relieve the pain.

11. 如果疼痛，请告诉我。

If you feel pain, please tell me.

12. 现在，您的牙齿已经拔下来了。

Now, your tooth has been pulled out.

13. 请咬紧棉球。

Please bite this gauze strongly.

14. 请咬棉球三十分钟。

Please bite on this gauze for thirty minutes.

15. 我另外给您一些棉球带回家，如果当您回家后拔牙创口继续出血，请换新棉球咬紧。

I will give you the extra gauze to take home, so please replace the gauze if bleeding does not stop.

....

16. 这是您的牙。您愿意保留它么？

This is your pulled out tooth. Would you like to keep your tooth？

....

17. 牙龈上有一个脓肿。

There is an abscess in the gum.

....

18. 我将切个小切口以便于脓液的引出。

I will make a small incision to drain the pus.

....

19. 我将给您缝合伤口。

I will suture.

....

20. 我将给您拆线。

I will take out the sutures.

（二十）Pediatric dentistry

儿童牙病的治疗

1. 今天我们会看看你的牙齿，并且会给它照相。

Today we are going to look at your teeth, and take pictures of them.

2. 我将会把你牙齿上的龋洞清理干净并用树脂充填它们。

I am going to clean a cavity in your tooth and fill it with composite resin.

3. 我将使你的牙齿睡觉。

I will make your tooth go to sleep.

4. 你不会有什么不舒服的感觉。

So you won't feel anything discomfortable.

5. 你的牙齿不会感觉到疼痛的。

It doesn't hurt at all.

6. 我不会把你弄痛的。

I won't hurt you.

7. 你仅仅能感觉到一点点痛。

You will feel a little pinch.

8. 如果你想让我停下来，你需要举起你的手。明白吗？

If you want me to stop, just raise your hand. Understand?

9. 这是喷水枪。

This is the water spray.

10. 我用气枪把你的牙齿吹干。

I'll make your teeth dry by air.

11. 我将用吸唾器吸净你的唾液。

I will use my vacuum cleaner to clean your mouth.

12. 请保持安静。

Please keep still.

13. 请漱口。

Please rinse your mouth.

14. 请稍微张点嘴。

Please open your mouth gently.

15. 张大嘴，舌头不要动。

Open your mouth wide and don't move your tongue.

16. 你喜欢糖吗？

Do you like sweet candies?

17. 牙虫也喜欢糖。

Tooth bugs like sweets, too.

18. 你口腔里小的细菌可以把糖变为酸。

Tiny germs in your mouth change sweets to acid.

19. 酸可以把你的牙齿弄个洞出来。

The acid can eat a cavity in the tooth.

20. 这些腐败的东西必须用牙钻清理干净，牙齿需要充填。

The decay has to be cleaned out by drilling and the tooth has to be filled.

21. 这些对预防龋病非常重要。

So，it is important to prevent tooth decay.

22. 我将用红色的液体涂抹你的牙齿以便我们能看到牙虫。

I will put a red color liquid on your teeth so that we can see the sugar bugs.

23. 拿着镜子看看你的牙齿。

Hold this mirror and look at your teeth.

24. 你要保证每顿饭后刷牙。

Will you promise to brush your teeth after meals?

25. 我给你的牙齿上涂一些氟以使它们更坚硬。

I will put some fluoride on your teeth to make them strong.

26. 我将吹干你的牙齿并给它们涂些氟化物。

I am going to dry and paint fluoride solution on your teeth.

27. 我将放些氟化物在这个海绵上，你把它含在嘴里约三分钟。

I will place some fluoride on this sponge and hold it in your mouth for three minutes.

28. 三十分钟内不要喝水和吃东西。

You should not drink or eat anything for thirty minutes.

29. 治疗很快就完了。

It will soon be finished.

30. 今天就这些。

That's all for today.

31. 你愿意再来看我们吗？

You'll come back see us again, won't you?

32. 今天你表现得非常好。

You've done very well today. Congratulations!

33. 很不幸，由于这颗牙根尖有脓肿，所以我们不能保留它。

Unfortunately, I can't conserve this tooth because of the abscess around the root tip.

34. 我必须拔除这颗乳牙。

I have to pull this milk tooth out.

35. 如果我们保留这颗牙，脓肿会影响恒牙的形成。

If we leave it, the infection pus might influence the formation of the following permanent tooth.

36. 被拔除两侧的牙会向缺牙处移动并减小间隙。

The teeth beside the extracted tooth will move and close the space.

37. 乳牙可以很好地为恒牙维持萌出间隙。

Milk teeth are the best to keep space for the permanent teeth.

38. 最好能把乳牙保留到替牙期。

It is better to keep milk teeth until their proper exchanging time.

39. 可以用缺隙保持器来维持缺失牙的间隙。

This appliance "a space maintainer" is used to hold teeth in place and will prevent from losing the space.

40. 规律的口腔检查对儿童来说非常必要。

It's absolutely necessary for your child to have regular dental check –ups.

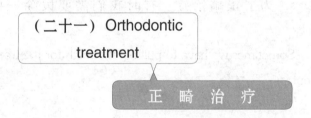

（二十一）Orthodontic treatment

正 畸 治 疗

1. 准确的诊断是正畸治疗所必需的。

Accurate diagnosis is necessary for orthodontic treatment.

2. 您的孩子是小下颌畸形。

Your child's jaw is very small.

3. 以后，您的孩子可能需要正畸治疗。

In the future, your child may need to have his teeth realigned (straightened).

....

4. 与颌骨相比，牙齿的体积显得太大。

The size of the teeth are too large compared with the size of the jaws.

....

5. 为了正畸治疗，有时我们需要拔除一些牙齿。

Sometimes we have to pull out the teeth for the treatment.

....

6. 正畸治疗不被包括在医疗保险内。

Orthodontic treatment is not covered by health insurance.

....

7. 正畸治疗需要很长时间。

It takes a long time to complete the orthodontic treatment.

8. 正畸治疗包括三个阶段，依次为：仔细检查，粘固锁槽调整，用保持器维持。

There are three stages for orthodontic treatment, the periods for detail examinations, treatment with braces and maintenance using a retainer.

9. 有固定矫治器和活动矫治器矫正牙齿。

There are fixed type and removable type appliance for straightening the teeth.

10. 由于托槽磨嘴唇和颊部，您可能会感觉不舒服。

You may feel uncomfortable with the braces, because they touch your cheek and lip.

11. 当正畸治疗时，您的牙齿可能会感觉敏感。

During the treatment with braces, you may feel some sensitivity.

12. 最好不要吃像糖一样粘的食物。

You had better not eat sticky food like a candy.

13. 正畸治疗不但可以改善容貌而且可以改善牙齿的功能。

The orthodontic treatment will improve not only the esthetic problems but also the function of the teeth.

（二十二）Instructions after treatments

各种治疗后的注意事项

| Instructions after filling
补牙后注意事项

1. 一小时内不要吃任何东西。

Don't eat anything for one hour.

2. 两小时内不要用您的右侧吃东西。

Don't chew on the right side of your mouth for at least two hours.

3. 小心不要咬到自己的舌头和嘴唇。

Be careful not to bite your tongue or lip.

4. 以后的一段时间，您的牙齿可能对冷食物敏感。

The tooth may be sensitive to cold food for a while.

5. 有大充填物的牙齿敏感很常见。

Sensitive is common in the tooth with a big filling.

6. 一周后敏感的症状将会消失。

It will disappear in about a week.

7. 对于龋洞近髓处，我们会用特殊的护髓材料保护牙髓。

I put a special lining over the deepest part of the cavity to protect the nerve of your tooth.

8. 我会用护髓材料来预防牙齿敏感。

I put a lining under the filling to prevent from sensitivity.

9. 以后有神经坏死的可能性。

There is a possibility that the nerve will die in the future.

10. 治疗后牙齿可能有点不舒服。

It might be a little uncomfortable after the treatment.

II Instructions after prosthetic treatment
修复后注意事项

1. 您会很快适应义齿的。

You will soon get accustomed to the dentures.

2. 睡觉前请拿下义齿。

Please take your denture out when you go to bed.

3. 当您不戴义齿时，请把它放到水里，防止义齿变干。

When you are not wearing your denture, be sure to keep them in a glass of water, so they will not become too dry.

4. 如果义齿干燥很长时间，它们可能变形失去好的适应性。

If they are dry for a long time, they may bend and lose their good fit.

....

III Instructions after teeth extraction
拔牙后注意事项

1. 压迫是最好的止血方法。

Pressure is one of the best treatments for bleeding.

....

2. 请紧咬棉球二十分钟直到止血。然后把棉球吐到塑料袋中系紧再丢入垃圾袋。

Please bite firmly on a piece of gauze for twenty minutes until it has stopped bleeding. Then place the used gauze in a plastic bag and tie tightly before disposing it in the rubbish

....

3. 拔牙后几天唾液里可能会带有少量血液。

It might bleed a little bit for the rest of the day.

4. 如果继续出血，请另外咬紧一个棉球。

If bleeding continues, place a piece of gauze over the extraction site and bite it firmly.

5. 直到明天口腔里有少量血液都是正常的。

It is normal for there to have a little bleeding mixed with saliva until the next day.

6. 如果继续出血和严重的疼痛，请立即与我们联系。

If you have any problems of bleeding and serious pain, please contact us immediately.

7. 直到完全止血后再漱口。

Don't start rinsing until the bleeding stops.

8. 二十四小时内不要漱口，漱口可能会影响凝血块的形成。

Don't rinse for twenty – four hours as it may disturb blood clot.

9．请不要用手指和舌头碰拔牙窝，它可能导致创口出血和感染。

Don't touch the extraction socket with a finger or tongue as it may lead to further bleeding and infection.

10．一小时后您可以用对侧吃些软食，不要吃硬的、热的和辛辣的食物。

You can eat about an hour after extraction but please chew on the other side of extraction and eat soft food. And avoid eating hard, hot and spicy food.

11．拔牙当天请不要洗澡和运动。

Avoid exercise and don't take a bath on the day of extraction.

12．拔牙当天请不要喝含酒精的饮料。

Don't drink alcoholic beverages on that day.

13. 如果麻药消失后继续疼痛，您可以用些我们建议的镇痛药。

If you have any pain following local anesthetic wearing off, please take painkillers as we advised.

14. 即使局部疼痛和肿胀，也不要用冰或冷水敷拔牙创。

Please don't place ice or cold water over the extraction area, even if you have pain or swelling.

15. 可能会肿胀几天。

There might be some swelling for a few days。

16. 肿胀两三天，请不要紧张。

Don't be surprised if there is some swelling for two or three days。

17. 你必须服用抗生素。

You have to take antibiotics.

18. 这样可以预防感染。

The purpose is to prevent infections.

19. 如果疼痛和肿胀，请给我们打电话。

Please telephone us, if you have pain or swelling.

20. 我认为你没有什么问题。

I don't think that you will have any trouble.

21. 明天我将冲洗您的伤口。

Tomorrow I want to irrigate the wound.

22. 一周后可以拆线。

The doctor will remove the sutures after a week.

23. 伤口完全愈合要一个月时间。

It will take about one month for the wound to heal.

（二十三）Medication

药 物 治 疗

1. 我将给您开些药。

I'll give you some medicine.

2. 这是镇痛药。

These are pain killers.

3. 如果您感觉疼痛可以服用一片镇痛药。

Take one painkiller if you are in pain.

4. 我将给您开三天的抗生素。

I will give you antibiotics for three days.

5. 每八小时服用两片药。

Take two tablets every eight hours.

6. 饭后服用两片药。

Take two tablets after every meal.

....

7. 饭后三十分钟用水服用抗生素，每天三次，连续服用三天。

Take this antibiotic with a glass of water thirty minutes after every meal, three times a day, for three days.

....

8. 必要时服用镇痛药。

Take the painkillers if necessary.

....

9. 一天内轻轻涂擦这种油膏几次。

Please rub this ointment gently several times in a day.

....

10. 这是您的处方，请到药房拿药。

This is a prescription. Take it to the pharmacy.

....

11. 我给您开些药，请按说明服用。

I'll write you a prescription, please take the medicine as instruction.

（二十四）At the reception

付 款 与 预 约

1. 今天的治疗费是 *300* 元。

The fee for today is 300 RMB.

2. 第一次检查费为 *110* 元。

Please pay the charge for the first examination, 110 RMB.

3. 这是您找回的 *50* 元钱。

Here's 50 RMB change.

4. 这是您的收据。

Here's your receipt.

5. 我将给您治疗的账单。

I'll send you the bill of your treatment.

6. 这是为您在美国的健康保险开的证明书。

This is the diagnosis for your American Health Insurance.

7. 保险公司给您报销。

The insurance company will reimburse you directly.

8. 我将把您约到一周后。

I'll give you an appointment for one week from today.

9. 下周一您能来复诊吗？

Can you return on Monday next week?

10. 上午，还是下午对您更方便？

Which is more convenient for you, morning or afternoon?

11. 明天两点可以吗？

How about two o'clock tomorrow.

12. 周五早晨九点复诊。

The next appointment is at nine a. m. on Friday.

13. 明天三点复诊。

We'll expect you at three o'clock tomorrow.

14. 请提前二十四小时取消预约。

Please try to cancel at least twenty-four hours before.

15. 可以通过电话预约。

Please call our clinic for an appointment.

16. 需要四次复诊或一个月的时间。

It will take four visits or one month to be treated.

17. 每次治疗大概需要三十分钟。

Each treatment will take about thirty minutes.

18. 两次以上的复诊是必需的。

At least two more visits are necessary.

19. 一周内复诊最好。

It will be better in about a week.

20. 如果病情加重，请与我们联系。

If there is any change for the worse, please contact with us.

21. 这是给大学附属医院的介绍信。

This is a letter of introduction to the university hospital.

22. 如果没有日常家庭的维护，治疗将会失败。

The treatment will fail without your daily home care.

23. 每年一次的口腔检查是非常重要的。

It is important to have regular dental check – ups at least once a year.

24. 六个月内我们将与您联系提醒您复诊。

We will be in touch with you in six months to remind you of your appointment by card.

....

25. 请小心。

Take care of yourself.

....